IT'S A MAGICAL WORLD

A Calvin and Hobbes Collection by Bill Watterson

Andrews McMeel
PUBLISHING®

Andrews McMeel Publishing
a division of Andrews McMeel Universal
1130 Walnut Street, Kansas City, Missouri 64106

www.andrewsmcmeel.com

ISBN: 978-0-7407-7796-7

Library of Congress Control Number: 96-83996

19 20 21 22 23 SDB 10 9 8 7 6

ATTENTION: SCHOOLS AND BUSINESSES

Andrews McMeel books are available at quantity discounts with bulk purchase for educational, business, or sales promotional use. For information, please e-mail the Andrews McMeel Publishing Special Sales Department: specialsales@amuniversal.com.

calvin and Hobbes by WATTERSON

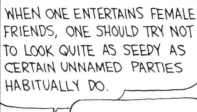

CALVIN and HOBBES
by WATTERSON

THE SECRET TO ENJOYING YOUR JOB IS TO HAVE A HOBBY THAT'S EVEN WORSE.

What was the significance of the Erie Canal?

IN tHE COSMIC SENSE, PRObabLY NiL.

WE "BIG PICTURE" PEOPLE RARELY BECOME HISTORIANS.

REMEMBER WHEN I WAS FIRST BORN? I COULDN'T EVEN TURN MYSELF OVER! MY EYES WOULDN'T FOCUS! I COULDN'T DO ANYTHING!

THINK OF ALL THE WORK IT TOOK TO DEVELOP THE MOTOR SKILLS NECESSARY TO HOLD A CRAYON, TO PLACE THE TIP OF IT ON A PAGE, AND TO MOVE IT IN PREDETERMINED, COORDINATED MOTIONS!

THIS PICTURE IS THE RESULT OF SIX YEARS' UNRELENTING TOIL! A LIFETIME OF EFFORT WENT INTO THIS!

I'M STILL NOT PAYING YOU $500 FOR IT.

IT WILL APPRECIATE! IT'S AN INVESTMENT!

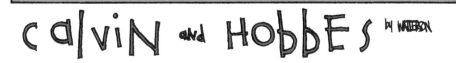

THIS NEW ISSUE OF *CHEWING* MAGAZINE TELLS HOW TO SET UP A MANDIBULAR FITNESS REGIME!

BASICALLY, THEY RECOMMEND INTERVAL TRAINING: CHEWING ONE PIECE OF GUM WITH LOTS OF REPS, FOLLOWED BY CHEWING FIVE PIECES OF GUM AT ONCE, SO YOU REALLY WORK THE MASSETER AND BUCCINATOR MUSCLES.

IT'S A GRUELING WORKOUT, BUT YOU BUILD STRENGTH **AND** ENDURANCE, SO YOU CAN COME THROUGH IN A CLINCHER.

I'M SURE THE GLORY MAKES IT ALL WORTHWHILE.

PLUS, YOU DEVELOP THAT "CHEWER'S JAW" THAT DRIVES THE GIRLS WILD.

WHAT'S WITH THE FACE?

I'M DOING STRETCHES.

CHEWING MAGAZINE SAYS YOU SHOULD ALWAYS WARM UP BEFORE YOU CHEW GUM.

DID YOU KNOW THAT NEGLECTING TO STRETCH THE TEMPORALIS MUSCLES IS THE LEADING CAUSE OF GUM CHEWING INJURIES?

WHAT ABOUT FALLING DOWN WHILE CHEWING AND WALKING?

WITH A GOOD HELMET, THE RISK IS SURPRISINGLY SMALL.

IN THIS ISSUE, *CHEWING* REVIEWS THE NEW GUM CHEWING APPAREL.

THIS JERSEY IS MADE WITH SWET-TEK® FIBERS THAT WICK AWAY PERSPIRATION! THE MESH COLLAR KEEPS YOUR STERNOMASTOIDS VENTILATED AND THE ZIPPERED POCKETS HOLD SPARE GUM AND WRAPPERS!

WHY IS IT COVERED WITH BRAND LOGOS?

THAT GIVES YOU THE PSYCHOLOGICAL EDGE OF PRETENDING YOU'RE SPONSORED.

HOW CAN YOU TELL IF YOU'RE READING AN ADVERTISEMENT, A PRODUCT REVIEW, OR THE PRODUCT ITSELF?

I'D SURE LIKE TO BE A WALKING ENDORSEMENT.

I NEED TO GET A HEART RATE MONITOR.

WHAT FOR?

TO MAKE SURE I'M CHEWING AT MY AEROBIC THRESHOLD! EVERY DAY I WANT TO SEE THAT I'M CHEWING MORE GUM FASTER, HARDER, AND LONGER!

WHAT'S THE POINT OF ATTACHING A NUMBER TO EVERYTHING YOU DO?

IF YOUR NUMBERS GO UP, IT MEANS YOU'RE HAVING MORE FUN.

SCIENCE TO THE SPIRIT'S RESCUE ONCE AGAIN.

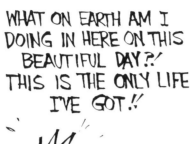

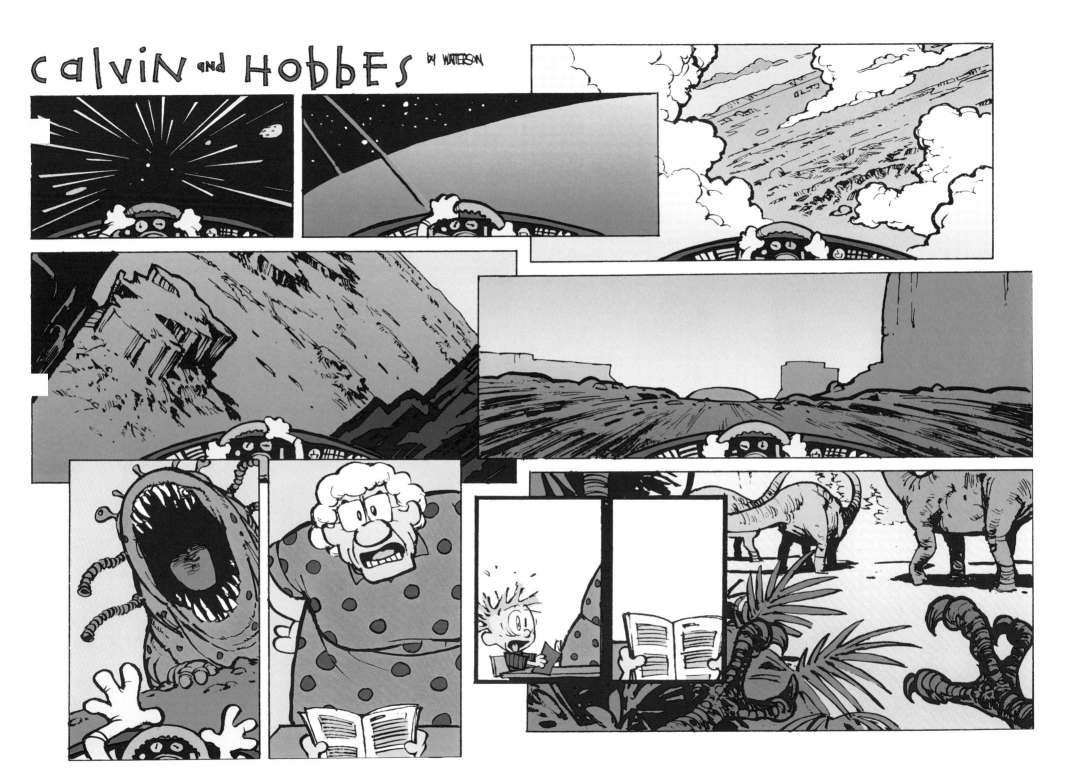

I HATE WHEN A LOT OF KIDS ARE ON THE SLIDE. YOU WAIT FOREVER TO GET TO THE TOP AND THEN THE RIDE IS OVER SO FAST.

AND IF YOU SIT FOR A MOMENT TO ENJOY THE HEIGHT, EVERYBODY YELLS AT YOU TO GET GOING.

AND SOMETIMES THE IDIOT BEHIND YOU STARTS DOWN TOO SOON AND HE SMACKS INTO YOU AT THE BOTTOM BEFORE YOU CAN GET AWAY.

YEP, THE PLAYGROUND IS A *LOT* MORE FUN AFTER CLASS STARTS.

CALVIN!

PHOOMPP

WHY ARE YOU CRYING?

I'M CUTTING UP AN ONION.

IT MUST BE HARD TO COOK IF YOU ANTHROPOMORPHIZE YOUR VEGETABLES.

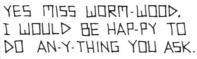

CalviN and HobbEs

by WATTERSON

37

ONE OF US SHOULD HAVE LEFT THE ROOM.

WHEN I WAS A KID, MY MOM WOULD TAKE ME TO THE BIG OLD DEPARTMENT STORE DOWNTOWN, AND I USED TO LOVE RIDING THE ESCALATORS.

THE ESCALATORS THERE HAD WOOD STAIRS, AND THEY USED TO CLICK, CLACK, AND CREAK. THE WOOD SLATS ON EACH STEP WERE MAYBE HALF AN INCH APART, AND I ALWAYS WONDERED IF LADIES GOT THEIR HIGH HEELS STUCK AND GOT PULLED UNDER.

SOME OF THOSE ESCALATORS WERE VERY NARROW—JUST WIDE ENOUGH FOR ONE PERSON. YEP, THOSE OLD ESCALATORS HAD A LOT MORE PERSONALITY THAN THESE SLICK METAL ONES.

I'D HATE TO THINK THAT ALL MY CURRENT EXPERIENCES WILL SOMEDAY BECOME STORIES WITH NO POINT.

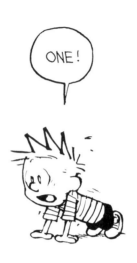

THINGS I WILL NEVER LIKE:

1. DRYING OFF WITH A COLD, DAMP TOWEL.
2. THE FEELING OF SEAWEED WRAPPING AROUND MY LEG.

3. ANYTHING THAT WAS POPULAR IN THE '70s.
4. LICORICE, YAMS, OR RAISINS.
5. THAT HIGH-PITCHED SCREECH THAT BABIES MAKE.
6. WRITHING MAGGOTS.

IT'S COMFORTING TO KNOW THAT THERE ARE CERTAINTIES IN LIFE.

LIFE IS FULL OF POSSIBILITIES.

FOR EXAMPLE, RIGHT NOW, INSTEAD OF WAITING FOR THE SCHOOL BUS, I COULD STICK OUT MY THUMB, HITCH A RIDE, AND SPEND THE REST OF MY LIFE IN THE SERENGETI, MIGRATING WITH THE WILDEBEESTS!

THE SERENGETI IS IN AFRICA. YOU COULDN'T REALLY HITCH A RIDE THERE.

LIFE IS FULL OF PRECLUDED POSSIBILITIES.

SLURRPP
SLUURRP

AACKKPTH
URGK BLUB

I'D BET ANYTHING THAT THE PRINCIPAL HAS A VALVE IN HIS OFFICE THAT CHANGES THE WATER PRESSURE.

WHY ARE YOU DIGGING A HOLE?

I'M LOOKING FOR BURIED TREASURE!

WHAT HAVE YOU FOUND?

A FEW DIRTY ROCKS, A WEIRD ROOT, AND SOME DISGUSTING GRUBS.

ON YOUR FIRST TRY??

THERE'S TREASURE EVERYWHERE!

45

WHEN BIRDS BURP, IT MUST TASTE LIKE BUGS.

NOBODY EVER PAYS ME A PENNY FOR MY THOUGHTS.

LOOK AT THIS, HOBBES. I ADDED IT UP AND FIGURED OUT I SPEND AN AVERAGE OF FOUR DAYS A YEAR TAKING BATHS!

FOUR FULL DAYS - MORNING, NOON, AND NIGHT - JUST SITTING IN THE STUPID BATHTUB! WHAT COULD POSSIBLY BE A BIGGER WASTE OF TIME THAN THAT ?!

HOW LONG DID IT TAKE YOU TO ADD THIS ALL UP?

IT'S HOT, IT'S HUMID, IT'S BUGGY, THERE'S NO BREEZE, AND THE AIR IS FULL OF POLLEN.

BUT IT'S *SUMMER!*

HEY ANT, YOU'RE WORKING LIKE A MANIAC AND WHAT HAVE YOU GOT TO SHOW FOR IT?

WHAT'S THE COLONY DONE FOR *YOU* LATELY? WHAT ABOUT *YOUR* NEEDS?

YOU DON'T OWE ANYBODY ANYTHING! LET THE OTHERS FEND FOR THEMSELVES! MOVE OUT! DISCOVER YOURSELF! EXPRESS YOUR INDIVIDUALITY!

IF THEY LISTEN, THIS SHOULD SOLVE OUR ANT PROBLEM.

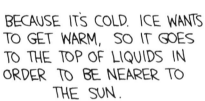

65

YOU THINK YOU'RE SO DARN SMART!

ART ISN'T ABOUT IDEAS. IT'S ABOUT STYLE.

THE MOST CRUCIAL CAREER DECISION IS PICKING A GOOD "ISM" SO EVERYONE KNOWS HOW TO CATEGORIZE YOU WITHOUT UNDERSTANDING THE WORK.

YOU DO GOOFY DRAWINGS ON THE SIDEWALK.

RIGHT. I'M A SUBURBAN POST-MODERNIST.

AREN'T WE ALL.

I WAS GOING TO BE A NEO-DECONSTRUCTIVIST BUT MOM WOULDN'T LET ME.

TIMES ARE TOUGH FOR US SUBURBAN POST-MODERNISTS.

HOW SO?

WELL, PEOPLE SEEM TO BE RELUCTANT TO PAY FOR SIDEWALK DRAWINGS THAT STAY WHERE THEY ARE AND WASH AWAY IN THE RAIN.

AND NOWADAYS, NOBODY WANTS TAX MONEY TO SUPPORT ART, AND CORPORATIONS WON'T UNDERWRITE ME BECAUSE I'M NOT FAMOUS ENOUGH TO EFFECTIVELY ADVERTISE THEIR CULTURAL ENLIGHTENMENT.

COULDN'T YOU SUPPORT YOUR ART WITH ANOTHER JOB?

WHAT, YOU MEAN **WORK**?

PEOPLE ALWAYS MAKE THE MISTAKE OF THINKING ART IS CREATED FOR THEM.

BUT REALLY, ART IS A PRIVATE LANGUAGE FOR SOPHISTICATES TO CONGRATULATE THEMSELVES ON THEIR SUPERIORITY TO THE REST OF THE WORLD.

AS MY ARTIST'S STATEMENT EXPLAINS, MY WORK IS UTTERLY INCOMPREHENSIBLE AND IS THEREFORE FULL OF DEEP SIGNIFICANCE.

YOU MISSPELLED "WELTANSCHAUUNG."

A GOOD ARTIST'S STATEMENT SAYS MORE THAN HIS ART EVER DOES.

..H-HOTT...

AHHHH

..NOT AGAIN...

73

PEOPLE ASK WHY WE TOLERATE A POPULAR CULTURE THAT CELEBRATES VIOLENCE AND DEPRAVITY.

BECAUSE IT'S ENTERTAINING, THAT'S WHY!

IF WARPED VALUES ARE THE PRICE OF A VICARIOUS THRILL, SO BE IT! LET THE BUSINESS RESPOND TO CONSUMER DEMAND!

THE CUSTOMER IS ALWAYS RIGHT.

SHOCK AND TITILLATE ME! I'VE GOT MONEY!

POPULAR CULTURE ISN'T TO BLAME FOR SELLING TWISTED VALUES.

MOVIES, RECORDS, AND TV SHOWS REFLECT THE REALITY OF OUR TIMES. ARTISTS DEPICT HATRED AND VIOLENCE BECAUSE THAT'S WHAT THEY SEE.

WHY DON'T THEY SEE THINGS OF BEAUTY AND VALUE?

BECAUSE BORING STUFF DOESN'T SELL.

SUCH VISION AND INTEGRITY.

THERE'S NOTHING LIKE A GOOD GUNFIGHT TO UPLIFT THE SPIRIT.

BUGS GET ON MY NERVES!

THE DIZZY WAY THEY ZIP AROUND, THE HIGH-PITCHED NOISE THEY MAKE, THEIR PESKY SIZE... EVERYTHING ABOUT THEM IS ANNOYING!

... SAID THE HYPERACTIVE, WHINY, SMALL CHILD.

!

I WANT YOU TO PICK UP YOUR ROOM TODAY, OK?

DO I GET PAID?

NO.

IF I DON'T GET PAID, HOW DO I KNOW IT'S IMPORTANT?!

YOU CAN TRUST A MOTHER ON THAT.

WE ALL WANT MEANINGFUL LIVES. WE LOOK FOR MEANING IN EVERYTHING WE DO.

BUT SUPPOSE THERE *IS* NO MEANING! SUPPOSE LIFE IS FUNDAMENTALLY ABSURD!

calvin and Hobbes by WATTERSON

SUPPOSE THERE'S NO REASON, OR TRUTH, OR RIGHTNESS IN ANYTHING!

I GUESS THERE'S NO HARM IN A LITTLE WISHFUL THINKING.

OR SUPPOSE *EVERYTHING* MATTERS. WHICH WOULD BE WORSE??

WHAT IF NOTHING MEANS ANYTHING? WHAT IF NOTHING REALLY MATTERS?

MY WATER BALLOON IS ROUND AND AERODYNAMIC FOR GRIM ACCURACY AND CERTAIN SOAKING!

YOUR WATER BALLOON IS LONG AND FLOPPY, IMPOSSIBLE TO THROW THE SLIGHTEST DISTANCE!

THE ADVANTAGE IS CLEARLY MINE! DO YOU SURRENDER?

HEY, THERE'S NO BUTTER IN THE BUTTER DISH! MY TOAST WILL GET COLD WHILE I GET ANOTHER STICK FROM THE FRIDGE!

HAVEN'T I SUFFERED ENOUGH?? WHERE WILL IT ALL END?!?

MR. AND MRS. EMPATHY.

WE RELY ON SIGHT TO CONFIRM THE EXISTENCE OF THINGS. WE DON'T BELIEVE IN THINGS WE CAN'T SEE.

SO HOW DO WE KNOW THAT NO-SEE-UMS EXIST? VERIFICATION IS RULED OUT BY DEFINITION!

IT'S AN ONTOLOGICAL QUANDARY.

HOLD STILL A MOMENT.

OOH, I ITCH!

GLAD I COULD HELP.

CALVIN, TIME TO COME IN!

AWW MOM, IT'S NOT EVEN DARK YET!

I DIDN'T SAY IT WAS. I SAID IT'S TIME TO COME IN.

IT'S A CRUEL SEASON THAT MAKES YOU GET READY FOR BED WHILE IT'S LIGHT OUT.

SOME PEOPLE ARE PRAGMATISTS, TAKING THINGS AS THEY COME AND MAKING THE BEST OF THE CHOICES AVAILABLE.

SOME PEOPLE ARE IDEALISTS, STANDING FOR PRINCIPLE AND REFUSING TO COMPROMISE.

AND SOME PEOPLE JUST ACT ON ANY WHIM THAT ENTERS THEIR HEADS.

I WONDER WHICH *YOU* ARE.

I PRAGMATICALLY TURN MY WHIMS INTO PRINCIPLES!

TO HELP MOM PREPARE BETTER MEALS, I'M COMPILING A BOOK OF RECIPES.

I NOTICE THAT ALL OF THEM INVOLVE DEEP-FAT FRYING.

I'M ADDING A CHOCOLATE SYRUP SECTION NOW.

IT USED TO BE THAT IF A CLIENT WANTED SOMETHING DONE IN A WEEK, IT WAS CONSIDERED A RUSH JOB, AND HE'D BE LUCKY TO GET IT.

NOW, WITH MODEMS, FAXES, AND CAR PHONES, EVERYBODY WANTS EVERYTHING INSTANTLY! IMPROVED TECHNOLOGY JUST INCREASES EXPECTATIONS.

THESE MACHINES DON'T MAKE LIFE EASIER — THEY MAKE LIFE MORE HARASSED.

SIX MINUTES TO MICROWAVE THIS?? WHO'S GOT THAT KIND OF TIME?!

IF WE WANTED MORE LEISURE, WE'D INVENT MACHINES THAT DO THINGS *LESS* EFFICIENTLY.

CalviN and HobbES

by WATTERSON

MY MOM AND MY DAD ARE NOT WHAT THEY SEEM.
THEIR DULL APPEARANCE IS PART OF THEIR SCHEME.
I KNOW OF THEIR PLANS. I KNOW THEIR TECHNIQUES.
MY PARENTS ARE OUTER SPACE ALIEN FREAKS!

THEY LANDED ON EARTH IN SPACESHIPS HUMONGOUS.
POSING AS GROWNUPS, THEY NOW WALK AMONG US.
MY PARENTS DENY THIS, BUT I KNOW THE TRUTH.
THEY'RE HERE TO ENSLAVE ME AND SPOIL MY YOUTH.

EARLY EACH MORNING, AS THE SUN RISES,
MOM AND DAD PUT ON THEIR EARTHLING DISGUISES.
I KNEW RIGHT AWAY THEIR MASKS WEREN'T LEGIT.
THEIR FACES ARE LINED — THEY SAG AND DON'T FIT.

THE EARTH'S GRAVITY MAKES THEM SLUGGISH AND SLOW.
THEY SAY NOT TO RUN, WHEREVER I GO.
THEY LIVE BY THE CLOCK. THEY'RE SLAVES TO ROUTINES.
THEY WORK THE YEAR 'ROUND. THEY'RE ALMOST MACHINES.

THEY DENY THAT TV AND FRIED FOOD HAVE MUCH WORTH.
THEY CANNOT BE HUMAN. THEY'RE NOT OF THIS EARTH.
I CANNOT ESCAPE THEIR ALIEN GAZE,
AND THEY'RE WARPING MY MIND WITH THEIR ALIEN WAYS.
FOR SINISTER PLOTS, THIS ONE IS A GEM.
THEY'RE BRINGING ME UP TO TURN *ME* INTO *THEM!*

I'M FILLING OUT A READER SURVEY FOR *CHEWING* MAGAZINE.

SEE, THEY ASKED HOW MUCH MONEY I SPEND ON GUM EACH WEEK, SO I WROTE, "$500." FOR MY AGE, I PUT "43", AND WHEN THEY ASKED WHAT MY FAVORITE FLAVOR IS, I WROTE "GARLIC / CURRY."

THIS MAGAZINE SHOULD HAVE SOME AMUSING ADS SOON.

I LOVE MESSING WITH DATA.

EVER NOTICE HOW PEOPLE ALWAYS TRY TO DO TWO THINGS AT ONCE?

THEY TALK ON THE PHONE WHILE THEY DRIVE, THEY WATCH TV WHILE THEY EAT, THEY LISTEN TO MUSIC WHILE THEY WORK...

PEOPLE NEVER FOCUS ON ANY ONE THING TO ENJOY IT OR DO IT WELL.

YOU'RE BREAKING MY CONCENTRATION.

WE FOCUS ON DOING NOTHING AT ALL!

calvin and HObbes by WATTERSON

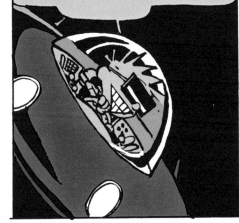

HERE'S STINKY, THE TALKING SOCK! HI, STINKY! SAY SOMETHING TO SUSIE!

HELLO, YOU UGLY BUCKET OF BOOGERS!

THAT DARN "THROW YOUR VOICE" AD MADE IT SOUND LIKE EVERYONE WOULD BE FOOLED.

THERE AREN'T MANY HEROES THESE DAYS.

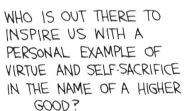

WHO IS OUT THERE TO INSPIRE US WITH A PERSONAL EXAMPLE OF VIRTUE AND SELF-SACRIFICE IN THE NAME OF A HIGHER GOOD?

WHO CAN WE LOOK UP TO? BUSINESS LEADERS? SPORTS FIGURES? POLITICIANS? CELEBRITIES? HECK, WE'RE LUCKY IF THEY DON'T END UP IN PRISON!

FORTUNATELY, IF WE CAN'T GET INSPIRATION, WE'LL ACCEPT ENTERTAINMENT.

AS USUAL, THE HERO BUSINESS IS UP TO ME.

OTHER KIDS' GAMES ARE ALL SUCH A BORE!
THEY'VE GOTTA HAVE RULES AND THEY GOTTA KEEP SCORE!
CALVINBALL IS BETTER BY FAR!
IT'S NEVER THE SAME! IT'S ALWAYS BIZARRE!
YOU DON'T NEED A TEAM OR A REFEREE!
YOU KNOW THAT IT'S GREAT, 'CAUSE IT'S NAMED AFTER ME!
IF YOU WANNA...

UH, FEEL FREE TO HARMONIZE WITH HOBBES ON THE RUMMA TUM TUMS.

THIS WAS A MISTAKE.

I'VE GOT THE CALVINBALL! EVERYBODY ELSE HAS TO GO IN SLOW MOTION NOW!

WAIT A MINUTE, CALVIN. I DON'T...

YOU HAVE TO **TALK** IN SLOW MOTION TOO. LIIIKE THISSS.

THIISSS GAAAAME MAAAKES NOOOO SENNNSE! IT'SSSS AASSS IFFFF YOU'RRRRE MAAAKINNNGGG IIIIIT UUUUP AAAS YOUUU GOOO.

HOBBES! SHE STUMBLED INTO THE PERIMETER OF WISDOM! RUN!!

OH...

CALVIN and HOBBES by WATTERSON

THE BIG, STUPID ULTRASAUR TAKES A LONG DRINK...

.. A *VERY* LONG DRINK!

THE FEROCIOUS ALLOSAUR IS THIRSTY TOO! THIS MEANS CONFRONTATION!

..AH HEH HEH..

FORTUNATELY, THIS ALLOSAUR IS THE PATIENT TYPE.

Don't make me smack you across the hall, twerp.

"ORIGINAL FLAVOR"... WAIT, HERE'S "LESS SODIUM," AND HERE'S "LITE," AND HERE'S "LESS FAT."

WHAT IF I WANT LESS FAT *AND* LESS SALT? WHAT DISTINGUISHES "LITE" FROM THESE OTHERS? DOES THE "ORIGINAL FLAVOR" PACKAGE IMPLY THAT THE OTHERS TASTE DIFFERENT?

FRANKLY, MY LIFE WAS PLENTY COMPLICATED *BEFORE* THE POTATO CHIPS.

LOOK AT ALL THIS PEANUT BUTTER! THERE MUST BE THREE SIZES OF FIVE BRANDS OF FOUR CONSISTENCIES! WHO DEMANDS THIS MUCH CHOICE??

I KNOW! I'LL QUIT MY JOB AND DEVOTE MY LIFE TO CHOOSING PEANUT BUTTER! IS "CHUNKY" CHUNKY ENOUGH, OR DO I NEED "*EXTRA*" CHUNKY"?

I'LL COMPARE INGREDIENTS! I'LL COMPARE BRANDS! I'LL COMPARE SIZES AND PRICES! MAYBE I'LL DRIVE AROUND AND SEE WHAT *OTHER* STORES HAVE! SO MUCH SELECTION AND SO LITTLE TIME!

I THINK *YOU* SHOULD DO THE SHOPPING.

DID THE MANAGER HAVE TO TALK TO YOU AGAIN?

HEY, WHERE'S THE PEANUT BUTTER?!

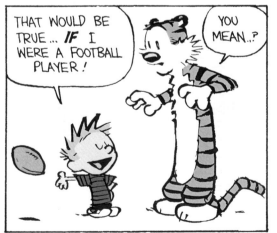

AND SO, AFTER A THREE MINUTE DOWNPOUR, HE BECAME LUDICROUSLY ATTIRED FOR THE REST OF THE DAY.

NOT EVERYONE CAN GET A FULL ISOMETRIC WORKOUT JUST BY YAWNING.

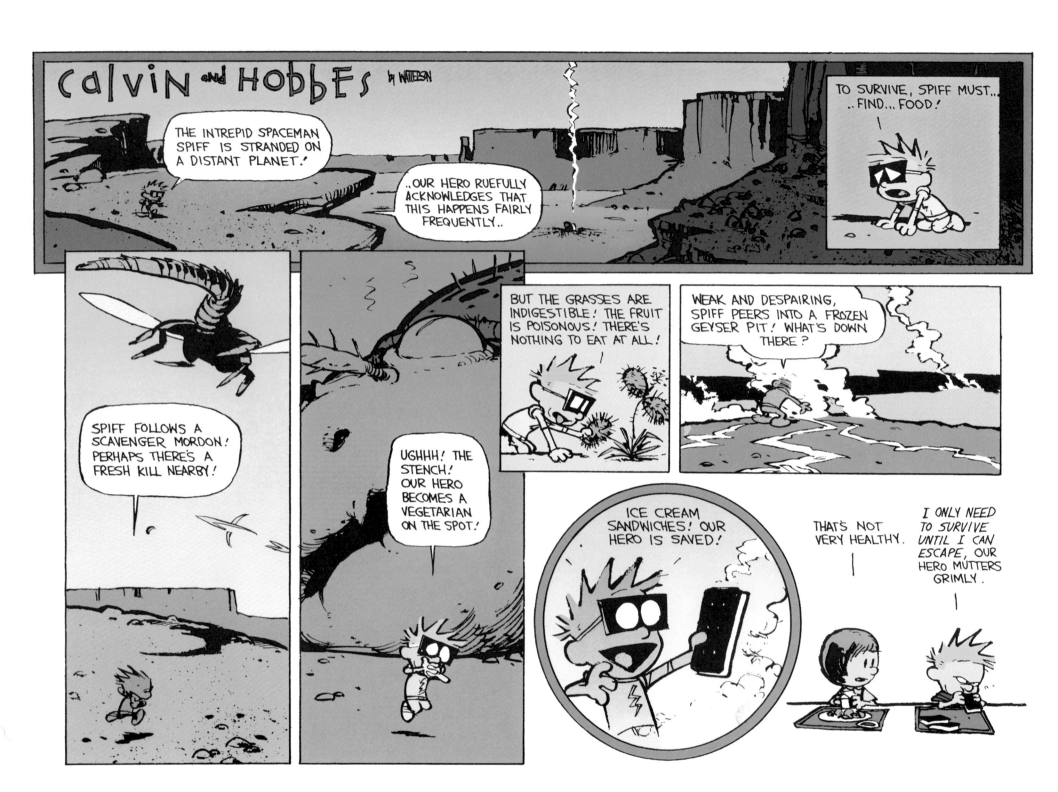

I WISH SCHOOL WOULD DISAPPEAR FOREVER, RIGHT NOW!

TO MAKE A BAD DAY WORSE, SPEND IT WISHING FOR THE IMPOSSIBLE.

UH OH, I FEEL A SNEEZE COMING ON.

AAA! NO TISSUE! NO HANKY! I.. AH.. AH... AH..

KACHOO!

OF MY LIMITED OPTIONS, THIS WAS PROBABLY THE WORST.

BOY, I HATE SCHOOL ASSIGNMENTS! MISS WORMWOOD IS OUT TO DESTROY MY LIFE!

WHAT DO YOU HAVE TO DO?

MAKE A LEAF COLLECTION! WHAT A DUMB WASTE OF TIME!

HOW MANY LEAVES DO YOU NEED?

50! I GOTTA COLLECT 50 LEAVES!

AND JUST WHEN I THOUGHT OF A LOOPHOLE, THE TEACHER SAID EVERY LEAF HAS TO BE A DIFFERENT KIND.

SHE'S GOT YOUR NUMBER.

WHEN DO YOU NEED TO PRESENT YOUR LEAF COLLECTION?

IN TWO WEEKS.

THAT'S NOT SO BAD. YOU JUST NEED THREE OR FOUR LEAVES A DAY.

I'M NOT WORKING ON WEEKENDS.

OK, FIVE LEAVES A DAY.

AND MY WEEKDAYS ARE BOOKED UNTIL NEXT THURSDAY AT 6 PM!

SO YOU NEED 50 LEAVES AN HOUR.

SEE?? IT'S IMPOSSIBLE!

OUR LEAF COLLECTIONS AREN'T DUE FOR A WEEK YET! HOW COULD YOU POSSIBLY BE ALMOST DONE ?!

I MAKE IT A GAME. I PRETEND IT'S A CONTEST TO SEE HOW MANY LEAVES I CAN FIND EACH DAY. THAT WAY, IT'S NOT AN ASSIGNMENT, IT'S FUN!

DID YOU KNOW THAT'S ONE OF THE TEN WARNING SIGNS OF HOPELESS DWEEBISM?

I'LL BET ANOTHER SIGN IS MOVING TO THE NEXT GRADE EACH YEAR.

THE TEACHER REMINDED US THAT WE ONLY HAVE A WEEK LEFT TO FINISH OUR LEAF COLLECTIONS, SO WE OUGHT TO BE HALF DONE NOW.

YOU HAVEN'T EVEN STARTED.

YEAH, BUT I WORK BETTER UNDER PRESSURE.

ACTUALLY, YOU WORK *ONLY* UNDER PRESSURE.

THAT WAY, THE WORK TIME IS MORE MISERABLE, BUT THERE'S LESS OF IT.

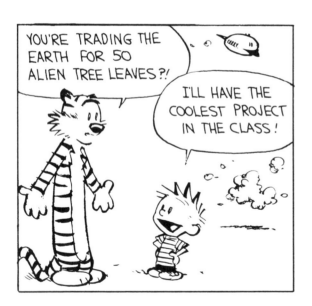

calvin and hobbes

by WATTERSON

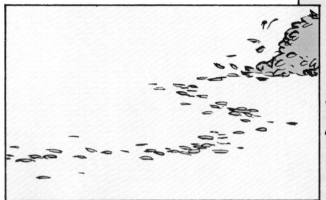

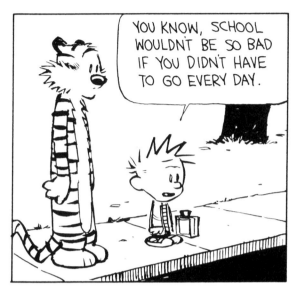

YOU KNOW, SCHOOL WOULDN'T BE SO BAD IF YOU DIDN'T HAVE TO GO EVERY DAY.

...AND IF YOU DIDN'T HAVE TO LEARN ANYTHING... AND IF YOU TOOK AWAY ALL THE TEACHERS AND ALL THE OTHER KIDS. IF IT WAS COMPLETELY DIFFERENT, SCHOOL WOULD BE GREAT.

A LOT OF THINGS ARE LIKE THAT.

NOBODY ASKS ME HOW THINGS OUGHT TO BE. I'VE GOT TONS OF IDEAS!

YES, CALVIN?

HEY KIDS, ON TOMORROW'S SHOW AND TELL, I'LL BE BRINGING A BIG SURPRISE! WILL IT SHOCK AND AMAZE YOU... **OR** WILL IT DISGUST AND TERRIFY YOU?? FIND OUT TOMORROW WHEN I REVEAL MY NEXT **SHOW AND TELL** HORROR! DON'T MISS IT!

RETURNING TO THE *LESSON*...

THAT'S CALLED A TEASER, BY THE WAY.

IN THE FUTURE, EVERYTHING WILL BE EFFORTLESS!

COMPUTERS WILL TAKE CARE OF EVERY TASK. WE'LL JUST POINT TO WHAT WE WANT DONE AND CLICK. WE'LL NEVER NEED TO LEAVE THE CLIMATE·CONTROLLED COMFORT OF OUR HOMES!

NO NUISANCE, NO WASTED TIME, NO ANNOYING HUMAN INTERACTION...

...NO LIFE.

LIFE IS TOO INCONVENIENT.

YOU'RE GOING TO JUGGLE EGGS?

IT'S A METAPHOR FOR LIFE, HOBBES.

EACH EGG REPRESENTS ONE OF LIFE'S CONCERNS AND THE GOAL IS TO GIVE EACH THE APPROPRIATE AMOUNT OF INDIVIDUAL ATTENTION WHILE SIMULTANEOUSLY WATCHING AND GUIDING ALL THE OTHERS.

LIFE IS ABOUT BALANCE AND STAYING QUICK AND ALERT AS EVERYTHING THREATENS TO SPIN OUT OF CONTROL!

AND SOMETIMES WE MAKE A BIG MESS OF THINGS.

BUT THE IMPORTANT THING IS PERSISTENCE.

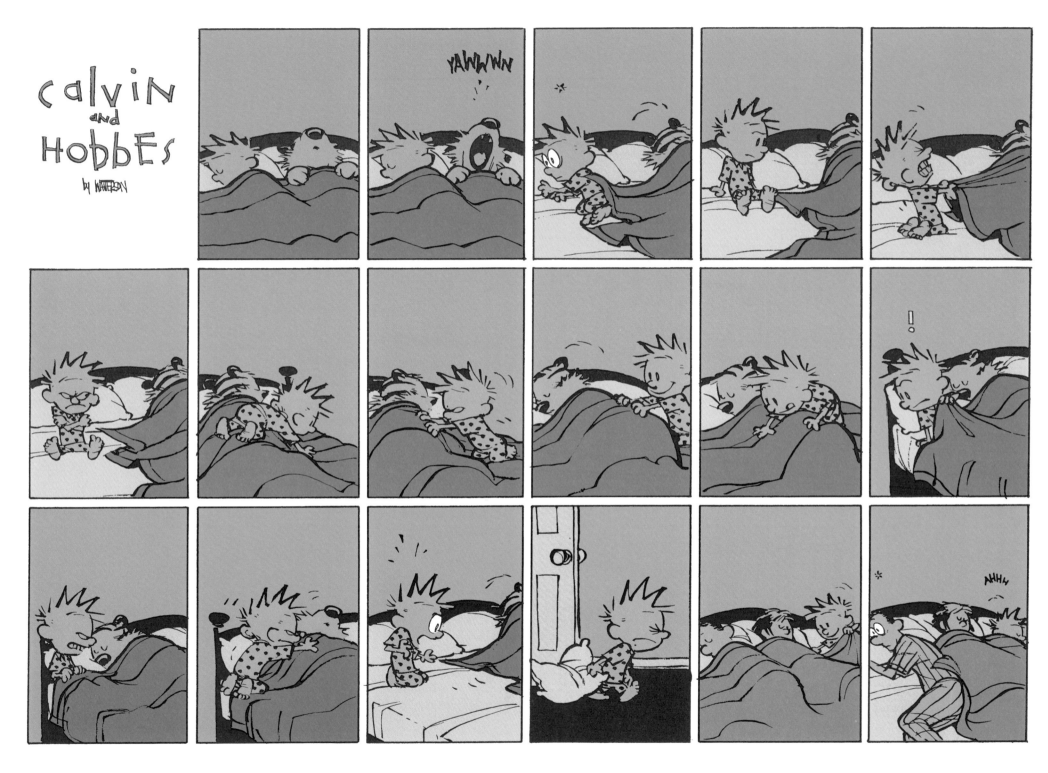

WHY ISN'T MY LIFE LIKE THIS SITUATION COMEDY?

WHY DON'T I HAVE A BUNCH OF FRIENDS WITH NOTHING TO DO BUT DROP BY AND INSTIGATE WACKY ADVENTURES?

WHY AREN'T MY CONVERSATIONS PEPPERED WITH SPONTANEOUS WITTICISMS? WHY DON'T MY FRIENDS DEMONSTRATE HEARTFELT CONCERN FOR MY WELL-BEING WHEN I HAVE PROBLEMS?

WHY DON'T YOU KNOW ANY GORGEOUS BABES?

I GOTTA GET MY LIFE SOME WRITERS.

KNOW WHAT'S WEIRD? DAY BY DAY NOTHING SEEMS TO CHANGE, BUT PRETTY SOON, EVERYTHING IS DIFFERENT.

YOU JUST GO ABOUT YOUR BUSINESS AND ONE DAY YOU REALIZE YOU'RE NOT THE SAME PERSON YOU USED TO BE. PEOPLE CHANGE WHETHER THEY DECIDE TO OR NOT!

THANK HEAVEN FOR SMALL FAVORS.

FOR EXAMPLE, I USED TO BE MORE TOLERANT OF OBLIQUE ASPERSIONS.

calviN and HobbEs by WATTERSON

AS A GENIUS, IT'S IMPORTANT THAT I WRITE A LOT OF LETTERS.

AFTER ALL, MY CORRESPONDENCE WILL BE THE BASIC RESOURCE MATERIAL FOR HISTORIANS TO RECONSTRUCT MY LIFE. MY WRITING WILL PROVIDE COUNTLESS FASCINATING INSIGHTS FOR BIOGRAPHERS.

SUCH AS HOW ALL YOUR SALUTATIONS BEGIN, "HEY BOOGERBRAIN."

IT'S BEEN THREE WEEKS AND I STILL HAVEN'T RECEIVED MY X-RAY GLASSES!

YIKES! NOT ANOTHER EXTREME CLOSE-UP ON SOMEBODY'S ANGUISH AND GRIEF!

WHY DO TV CAMERAS ZOOM IN SO CLOSE TO PEOPLE'S FACES THAT YOU CAN'T EVEN SEE THEIR ENTIRE HEADS?! DO THEY THINK WE CAN'T READ THE PERSON'S EXPRESSION FROM MORE THAN TWO INCHES AWAY?!

WHAT A VIOLATION OF PERSONAL SPACE! WHAT A SHAMELESS INTRUSION! WHAT A HEARTLESS ASSAULT ON HUMAN DIGNITY!

WHY ARE YOU STANDING AGAINST THE WALL?

I'M WATCHING TV.

BRRR, IT'S FREEZING OUT THERE! I DON'T WANT TO LEAVE MY NICE WARM BED.

ON DAYS LIKE THIS, I WISH MOM WOULD COME IN, LAY AN EXTRA BLANKET OVER ME, PAT MY HEAD, AND AS I SINK INTO THE PILLOW UNDER THE WEIGHT OF THE COVERS, SHE'D SAY...

HEY, LET'S *MOVE* IT !!! THIS IS THE THIRD TIME I'VE CALLED YOU! YOU'RE GOING TO MISS THE BUS! LET'S GO!!!

THESE MORNINGS ARE GOING TO KILL ME.

THE PACE OF MODERN LIFE IS ALL WRONG. IT MAKES EVERY DAY AN ORDEAL. EVERYBODY'S EXHAUSTED, STRESSED OUT, AND SHORT-TEMPERED!

LOOK AT ME! WHY AM I WAITING FOR A BUS AT THIS HORRIBLE HOUR ?! IT'S UNNATURAL AND UNHEALTHY!

WE SHOULD *EASE* INTO THE DAY! YOU KNOW, READ THE PAPER, HAVE SOME HOT COCOA, GO FOR A LEISURELY WALK AND GET OUR THOUGHTS TOGETHER ...

SO NOW IT'S MID-AFTERNOON.

RIGHT. TIME TO KICK BACK FOR A LITTLE SIESTA AND PLAN DINNER.

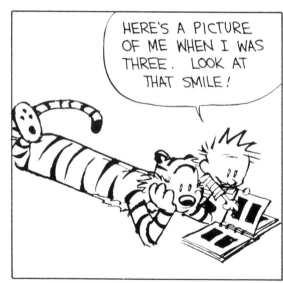

calvin and Hobbes by WATTERSON

EVER NOTICE HOW MANY CONVERSATIONS REVOLVE AROUND TV SHOWS AND MOVIES?

OUR COMMON REFERENCES ARE EVENTS THAT NEVER HAPPENED AND PEOPLE WE'LL NEVER MEET.' WE KNOW MORE ABOUT CELEBRITIES AND FICTIONAL CHARACTERS THAN WE KNOW ABOUT OUR NEIGHBORS!

THAT MUST BE WHY NEW HOUSES AREN'T BUILT WITH BIG FRONT PORCHES ANYMORE.

I CAN'T BELIEVE DAD WON'T LET ME HAVE A TV IN MY OWN ROOM.

I LIKE THE SOUND OF SLEET HITTING THE WINDOW PANES AT NIGHT.

AND I LIKE WHEN THE SLEET TURNS TO HEAVY SNOW AS IT GETS COLDER, SO YOU KNOW THAT TOMORROW THE WORLD WILL BE BURIED IN ICE AND SNOW!

IT'S ONE OF THE FEW PLEASURES RESERVED FOR THOSE WHO DON'T DRIVE.

I *KNEW* I SHOULD'VE THROWN THAT SNOWBALL SOONER!

DEAR Santa,
Hi, it's ME, Calvin.

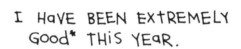

I HAVE BEEN EXTREMELY GOOD* THIS YEAR.

OBVIOUSLY, YOU'RE HOPING SANTA WON'T READ THE LONG, FINE PRINT DISCLOSURE IN THE FOOTNOTE.

I GOT THE IDEA FROM CAR ADS.

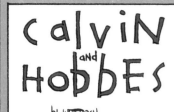

WITH 200 SNOWBALLS AT MY IMMEDIATE DISPOSAL, I HAVE NO OPPOSITION! MY WILL IS LAW! I AM OMNIPOTENT!

HOW BORING.

IN THE *SHORT* TERM, IT WOULD MAKE ME HAPPY TO GO PLAY OUTSIDE.

IN THE *LONG* TERM, IT WOULD MAKE ME HAPPIER TO DO WELL AT SCHOOL AND BECOME SUCCESSFUL.

BUT IN THE *VERY* LONG TERM, I KNOW WHICH WILL MAKE BETTER MEMORIES.

157

THE CHRISTMAS SEASON IS ALWAYS A TIME FOR PERSONAL REFLECTION.

TOO OFTEN WE DON'T EXAMINE OUR LIVES. THIS IS A TIME TO TAKE STOCK AND THINK ABOUT WHAT'S IMPORTANT.

IT'S A TIME TO REDEDICATE ONESELF TO FRENZIED ACQUISITION..., A TIME TO SPREAD THE JOY OF MATERIAL WEALTH... A TIME TO GLORIFY PERSONAL EXCESS OF EVERY KIND!

EARTHLY REWARDS MAKE CONSUMERISM A POPULAR RELIGION.

...A TIME TO ATONE FOR ONE'S FRUGALITY!

OH BOY, LOOK AT ALL THE SNOW! IT MUST BE SIX INCHES DEEP!

THIS WILL BE PERFECT FOR SLEDDING OR...

DING DONG

DING DONG DING DONG

ALL RIGHT! I'M COMING! I'M COMING!

WHAT THE HECK IS WRONG WITH THIS PLANET YOU SOLD US?!

THE ALIENS DIDN'T KNOW ABOUT WINTER?

THEY CLAIM I SOLD THEM A PLANET WITH A FAULTY AXIS! WHAT SHOULD I DO?

OFFER A REFUND. GIVE BACK THEIR LEAF COLLECTION.

ARRGGH! I THREW IT AWAY WHEN IT GOT SUCH A BAD GRADE!

HMM... WELL, WE SHOULD AT LEAST HELP THEM STAY WARM THEN.

BUT WHAT COULD THEY WEAR? THEY DON'T EVEN HAVE ARMS! ..THEY NEED HUGE SOCKS OR SOMETHING!

HEY! NO! BAD IDEA! BAD IDEA!

OOH, THIS IS TOASTY!

THANK YOU, EARTH LEADER!

THAT'S MY CHRISTMAS STOCKING!

THEY'RE GOING AWAY WITH OUR STOCKINGS! SANTA CAN'T FILL 'EM WITH LOOT!

I'M SURE SANTA KNOWS WE DID A NICE THING AND HE'LL WORK IT ALL OUT.

HEY YEAH, I DID SOMETHING GOOD! WE'RE TALKING JACKPOT! WE'RE TALKING MULTIPLE TRIPS FROM THE POLE TO HAUL IT ALL!

YOUR SELFLESSNESS IS THE HOPE OF THE SEASON.

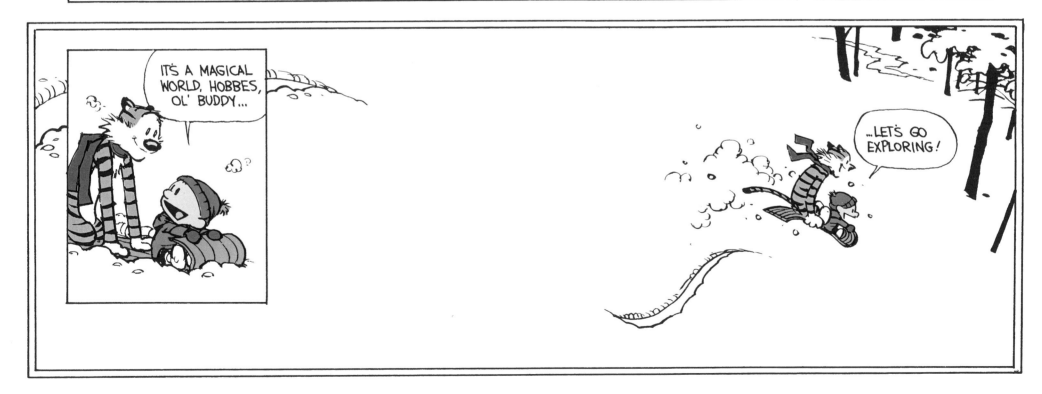